WITH
GOD'S HELP

I Will

- THIS JOURNAL BELONGS TO -

_____

Scripture quotations are taken from the *Holy Bible*, New Living Translation, copyright ©1996, 2004, 2015 by Tyndale House Foundation. Used by permission of Tyndale House Publishers, Inc., Carol Stream, Illinois 60188. All rights reserved.

Published by Erica N. Williams, LLC, Woodbridge, VA
Cover and Interior Design: Erica N. Williams

Printed in the United States of America
ISBN: 978-0-578-85420-5 (Paperback)

Hey, Gorgeous!

Welcome! This purity journal is filled with activities I find helpful in walking out purity. You see, in 2011, when I decided to pursue purity, I didn't know how to go about doing it, I just knew I wanted to honor God. I struggled in the beginning, but I found healing through prayer, meditating on God's word and writing.

It is my prayer that as you dive into this journal, you will grow in your walk with Christ and gain wisdom and strength to remain focused and committed to your journey to purity®. You are more than enough. God thought so much of you that He sent His Son Jesus to die for you. Be encouraged. If you were worth Jesus dying for, then surely, you're worth waiting for.

This journal includes 14 unique pages of writing prompts:
- My Reflection - Reflect on Bible verse & answer questions
- Celebrate My Wins - Recognize milestones reached on journey
- My Personal Prayers - Record your prayers for others
- Abba Father - Make your requests known to God
- Areas for Growth - Identify areas in which you need to improve
- Moment of Reflection - Reflect on your week & answer questions
- Unlined Pages - Write or draw whatever is on your heart
- Notes - Jot down sermon notes, quotes, answered prayers, etc.

I have no doubt that as you utilize this journal, you will be amazed at the clarity with which you will begin to hear from God as you endeavor to pursue purity and holiness. Remember, with God's help you will!

Are you ready?

Dig in!

Psalms 108:13

With God's help we will do mighty things, for He will trample down our foes.

"DON'T COPY THE BEHAVIOR AND CUSTOMS OF THIS WORLD, BUT LET GOD TRANSFORM YOU INTO A NEW PERSON BY CHANGING THE WAY YOU THINK. THEN YOU WILL LEARN TO KNOW GOD'S WILL FOR YOU, WHICH IS GOOD AND PLEASING AND PERFECT."
– ROMANS 12:2 –

My Reflection

_____

_____

_____

_____

_____

_____

_____

_____

_____

_____

_____

_____

_____

_____

_____

_____

_____

_____

_____

_____

_____

WEEK 1: _____

WHAT IS THIS PASSAGE TEACHING?

_____

_____

_____

_____

_____

HOW CAN I APPLY WHAT I HAVE LEARNED TO MY LIFE?

_____

_____

_____

_____

_____

WHAT IS HOLDING ME BACK FROM TAKING ACTION?

_____

_____

_____

_____

_____

MY PERSONAL PRAYER TO GOD

_____

_____

_____

_____

_____

Celebrate My Wins

WINS I AM THANKFUL FOR

1. _____
2. _____
3. _____
4. _____
5. _____

PEOPLE WHO HAVE HELPED ALONG THE WAY

1. _____
2. _____
3. _____
4. _____
5. _____

GREATEST LESSON LEARNED

_____
_____
_____
_____
_____
_____

WEEK 2: _____

WHY DO I *celebrate* THESE WINS?

_____
_____
_____
_____
_____
_____
_____
_____
_____
_____
_____

HOW CAN I *help* OTHERS WIN?

_____
_____
_____
_____
_____
_____
_____
_____
_____

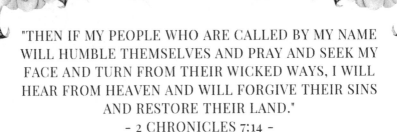

"THEN IF MY PEOPLE WHO ARE CALLED BY MY NAME
WILL HUMBLE THEMSELVES AND PRAY AND SEEK MY
FACE AND TURN FROM THEIR WICKED WAYS, I WILL
HEAR FROM HEAVEN AND WILL FORGIVE THEIR SINS
AND RESTORE THEIR LAND."
- 2 CHRONICLES 7:14 -

My Personal Prayers...

FOR MY LOVED ONES

_____
_____
_____
_____
_____
_____
_____

FOR MY COLLEAGUES

_____
_____
_____
_____
_____
_____

WEEK 3: _____

FOR MY CITY

_____

_____

_____

_____

_____

FOR MY STATE

_____

_____

_____

_____

_____

FOR MY NATION

_____

_____

_____

_____

_____

FOR THE WORLD

_____

_____

_____

_____

_____

"ABBA, FATHER," HE CRIED OUT, "EVERYTHING IS POSSIBLE
FOR YOU. PLEASE TAKE THIS CUP OF SUFFERING AWAY
FROM ME. YET I WANT YOUR WILL TO BE DONE, NOT MINE."
- MARK 14:36 -

Abba Father,

DRAW ME CLOSER TO

_____

_____

_____

_____

_____

LEAD ME AWAY FROM

_____

_____

_____

_____

INCREASE MY DISCERNMENT IN

_____

_____

_____

_____

_____

_____

WEEK 4: _____

GIVE ME WISDOM TO

_____
_____
_____
_____
_____
_____
_____
_____
_____

GIVE ME STRENGTH TO

_____
_____
_____
_____
_____
_____
_____
_____
_____
_____

"SO WE HAVE NOT STOPPED PRAYING FOR YOU SINCE
WE FIRST HEARD ABOUT YOU. WE ASK GOD TO GIVE
YOU COMPLETE KNOWLEDGE OF HIS WILL AND TO
GIVE YOU SPIRITUAL WISDOM AND UNDERSTANDING."
- COLOSSIANS 1:9 -

Areas for Growth

5 THINGS I STRUGGLE WITH

1. _____
2. _____
3. _____
4. _____
5. _____

5 LIES I BELIEVE ABOUT ME

1. _____
2. _____
3. _____
4. _____
5. _____

5 TRUTHS GOD'S WORD REVEALS ABOUT ME

1. _____
2. _____
3. _____
4. _____
5. _____

WEEK 5: _____

5 SCRIPTURES TO MEDITATE ON

1. _____
2. _____
3. _____
4. _____
5. _____

5 DECLATIONS TO SPEAK OVER MY LIFE

1. _____
2. _____
3. _____
4. _____
5. _____

5 THINGS I AM BELIEVING GOD FOR

1. _____
2. _____
3. _____
4. _____
5. _____

5 WAYS I CAN SHARE MY FAITH IN JESUS WITH OTHERS

1. _____
2. _____
3. _____
4. _____
5. _____

"INSTEAD, LET US TEST AND EXAMINE OUR WAYS.
LET US TURN BACK TO THE LORD."
- LAMENTATIONS 3:40 -

Moment of Reflection

I REMAINED FOCUSED BY

_____

_____

_____

_____

_____

I AVOIDED DISTRACTIONS BY

_____

_____

_____

_____

_____

I FELT GOD'S LOVE WHEN

_____

_____

_____

_____

WEEK 6: _____

I PRAISED GOD FOR

_____

_____

_____

_____

_____

I ASKED FORGIVENESS FOR

_____

_____

_____

_____

_____

I AM LOOKING FORWARD TO

_____

_____

_____

_____

_____

"DON'T YOU REALIZE THAT YOUR BODY IS THE TEMPLE OF THE HOLY SPIRIT, WHO LIVES IN YOU AND WAS GIVEN TO YOU BY GOD? YOU DO NOT BELONG TO YOURSELF, FOR GOD BOUGHT YOU WITH A HIGH PRICE. SO YOU MUST HONOR GOD WITH YOUR BODY."
- 1 CORINTHIANS 6:19-20 -

My Reflection

_____
_____
_____
_____
_____
_____
_____
_____
_____
_____
_____
_____
_____
_____
_____
_____
_____
_____
_____
_____

WEEK 7: _____

WHAT IS THIS PASSAGE TEACHING?

_____

_____

_____

_____

_____

HOW CAN I APPLY WHAT I HAVE LEARNED TO MY LIFE?

_____

_____

_____

_____

WHAT IS HOLDING ME BACK FROM TAKING ACTION?

_____

_____

_____

_____

MY PERSONAL PRAYER TO GOD

_____

_____

_____

_____

Celebrate My Wins

WINS I AM THANKFUL FOR

1. _____
2. _____
3. _____
4. _____
5. _____

PEOPLE WHO HAVE HELPED ALONG THE WAY

1. _____
2. _____
3. _____
4. _____
5. _____

GREATEST LESSON LEARNED

_____
_____
_____
_____
_____
_____

WEEK 8: _____

WHY DO I *celebrate* THESE WINS?

_____
_____
_____
_____
_____
_____
_____
_____
_____
_____

HOW CAN I *help* OTHERS WIN?

_____
_____
_____
_____
_____
_____
_____
_____
_____
_____

My Personal Prayers...

FOR MY LOVED ONES

_____

_____

_____

_____

_____

_____

_____

FOR MY COLLEAGUES

_____

_____

_____

_____

_____

_____

_____

WEEK 9: _____

FOR MY CITY

_____

_____

_____

_____

_____

FOR MY STATE

_____

_____

_____

_____

_____

FOR MY NATION

_____

_____

_____

_____

_____

FOR THE WORLD

_____

_____

_____

_____

_____

Abba Father,

DRAW ME CLOSER TO

_____

_____

_____

_____

_____

LEAD ME AWAY FROM

_____

_____

_____

_____

INCREASE MY DISCERNMENT IN

_____

_____

_____

_____

_____

_____

WEEK 10: _____

GIVE ME WISDOM TO

_____

_____

_____

_____

_____

_____

_____

_____

_____

_____

GIVE ME STRENGTH TO

_____

_____

_____

_____

_____

_____

_____

_____

_____

_____

_____

"LIKE NEWBORN BABIES, YOU MUST CRAVE PURE
SPIRITUAL MILK SO THAT YOU WILL GROW INTO A
FULL EXPERIENCE OF SALVATION. CRY OUT FOR THIS
NOURISHMENT,"
- 1 PETER 2:2 -

Areas for Growth

5 THINGS I STRUGGLE WITH

1. _____
2. _____
3. _____
4. _____
5. _____

5 LIES I BELIEVE ABOUT ME

1. _____
2. _____
3. _____
4. _____
5. _____

5 TRUTHS GOD'S WORD REVEALS ABOUT ME

1. _____
2. _____
3. _____
4. _____
5. _____

WEEK 11: _____

5 SCRIPTURES TO MEDITATE ON

1. _____
2. _____
3. _____
4. _____
5. _____

5 DECLATIONS TO SPEAK OVER MY LIFE

1. _____
2. _____
3. _____
4. _____
5. _____

5 THINGS I AM BELIEVING GOD FOR

1. _____
2. _____
3. _____
4. _____
5. _____

5 WAYS I CAN SHARE MY FAITH IN JESUS WITH OTHERS

1. _____
2. _____
3. _____
4. _____
5. _____

"FOR GOD HAS NOT GIVEN US A SPIRIT OF FEAR AND
TIMIDITY, BUT OF POWER, LOVE, AND SELF-DISCIPLINE."
- 2 TIMOTHY 1:7 -

Moment of Reflection

I REMAINED FOCUSED BY

_____
_____
_____
_____
_____

I AVOIDED DISTRACTIONS BY

_____
_____
_____
_____
_____

I FELT GOD'S LOVE WHEN

_____
_____
_____
_____

WEEK 12: _____

I PRAISED GOD FOR

_____

_____

_____

_____

_____

I ASKED FORGIVENESS FOR

_____

_____

_____

_____

_____

I AM LOOKING FORWARD TO

_____

_____

_____

_____

_____

"SEARCH ME, O GOD, AND KNOW MY HEART; TEST ME
AND KNOW MY ANXIOUS THOUGHTS. POINT OUT
ANYTHING IN ME THAT OFFENDS YOU, AND LEAD ME
ALONG THE PATH OF EVERLASTING LIFE."
- PSALMS 139:23-24 -

My Reflection

_____

_____

_____

_____

_____

_____

_____

_____

_____

_____

_____

_____

_____

_____

_____

_____

_____

_____

WEEK 13: _____

WHAT IS THIS PASSAGE TEACHING?

_____

_____

_____

_____

_____

HOW CAN I APPLY WHAT I HAVE LEARNED TO MY LIFE?

_____

_____

_____

_____

_____

WHAT IS HOLDING ME BACK FROM TAKING ACTION?

_____

_____

_____

_____

_____

MY PERSONAL PRAYER TO GOD

_____

_____

_____

_____

_____

Celebrate My Wins

WINS I AM THANKFUL FOR

1. _____
2. _____
3. _____
4. _____
5. _____

PEOPLE WHO HAVE HELPED ALONG THE WAY

1. _____
2. _____
3. _____
4. _____
5. _____

GREATEST LESSON LEARNED

_____
_____
_____
_____
_____
_____

WEEK 14: _____

WHY DO I *celebrate* THESE WINS?

_____
_____
_____
_____
_____
_____
_____
_____
_____
_____

HOW CAN I *help* OTHERS WIN?

_____
_____
_____
_____
_____
_____
_____
_____
_____
_____

My Personal Prayers...

FOR MY LOVED ONES

_____

_____

_____

_____

_____

_____

_____

_____

FOR MY COLLEAGUES

_____

_____

_____

_____

_____

_____

_____

WEEK 15: _____

FOR MY CITY

_____

_____

_____

_____

_____

FOR MY STATE

_____

_____

_____

_____

_____

FOR MY NATION

_____

_____

_____

_____

_____

FOR THE WORLD

_____

_____

_____

_____

_____

"THERE IS SALVATION IN NO ONE ELSE! GOD HAS GIVEN NO
OTHER NAME UNDER HEAVEN BY WHICH WE MUST BE
SAVED."
- ACTS 4:12 -

Abba Father,

DRAW ME CLOSER TO

_____

_____

_____

_____

_____

LEAD ME AWAY FROM

_____

_____

_____

_____

INCREASE MY DISCERNMENT IN

_____

_____

_____

_____

_____

_____

WEEK 16: _____

GIVE ME WISDOM TO

_____

_____

_____

_____

_____

_____

_____

_____

_____

GIVE ME STRENGTH TO

_____

_____

_____

_____

_____

_____

_____

_____

_____

_____

"AND I AM CERTAIN THAT GOD, WHO BEGAN THE
GOOD WORK WITHIN YOU, WILL CONTINUE HIS WORK
UNTIL IT IS FINALLY FINISHED ON THE DAY WHEN
CHRIST JESUS RETURNS."
- PHILIPPIANS 1:6 -

Areas for Growth

5 THINGS I STRUGGLE WITH

1. _____
2. _____
3. _____
4. _____
5. _____

5 LIES I BELIEVE ABOUT ME

1. _____
2. _____
3. _____
4. _____
5. _____

5 TRUTHS GOD'S WORD REVEALS ABOUT ME

1. _____
2. _____
3. _____
4. _____
5. _____

WEEK 17: _____

5 SCRIPTURES TO MEDITATE ON

1. _____
2. _____
3. _____
4. _____
5. _____

5 DECLATIONS TO SPEAK OVER MY LIFE

1. _____
2. _____
3. _____
4. _____
5. _____

5 THINGS I AM BELIEVING GOD FOR

1. _____
2. _____
3. _____
4. _____
5. _____

5 WAYS I CAN SHARE MY FAITH IN JESUS WITH OTHERS

1. _____
2. _____
3. _____
4. _____
5. _____

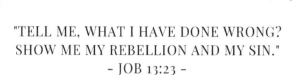

"TELL ME, WHAT I HAVE DONE WRONG?
SHOW ME MY REBELLION AND MY SIN."
- JOB 13:23 -

Moment of Reflection

I REMAINED FOCUSED BY

_____
_____
_____
_____
_____

I AVOIDED DISTRACTIONS BY

_____
_____
_____
_____
_____

I FELT GOD'S LOVE WHEN

_____
_____
_____
_____

WEEK 18: _____

I PRAISED GOD FOR

_____

_____

_____

_____

_____

I ASKED FORGIVENESS FOR

_____

_____

_____

_____

_____

I AM LOOKING FORWARD TO

_____

_____

_____

_____

_____

"GUARD YOUR HEART ABOVE ALL ELSE, FOR IT
DETERMINES THE COURSE OF YOUR LIFE."
- PROVERBS 4:23 -

My Reflection

_____

_____

_____

_____

_____

_____

_____

_____

_____

_____

_____

_____

_____

_____

_____

_____

_____

_____

WEEK 19: _____

WHAT IS THIS PASSAGE TEACHING?

_____
_____
_____
_____
_____

HOW CAN I APPLY WHAT I HAVE LEARNED TO MY LIFE?

_____
_____
_____
_____
_____

WHAT IS HOLDING ME BACK FROM TAKING ACTION?

_____
_____
_____
_____
_____

MY PERSONAL PRAYER TO GOD

_____
_____
_____
_____
_____

Celebrate My Wins

WINS I AM THANKFUL FOR

1. _____
2. _____
3. _____
4. _____
5. _____

PEOPLE WHO HAVE HELPED ALONG THE WAY

1. _____
2. _____
3. _____
4. _____
5. _____

GREATEST LESSON LEARNED

_____
_____
_____
_____
_____
_____

WEEK 20: _____

WHY DO I *celebrate* THESE WINS?

_____
_____
_____
_____
_____
_____
_____
_____
_____
_____

HOW CAN I *help* OTHERS WIN?

_____
_____
_____
_____
_____
_____
_____
_____
_____
_____

"IF YOU SEE A FELLOW BELIEVER SINNING IN A WAY THAT DOES NOT LEAD TO DEATH, YOU SHOULD PRAY, AND GOD WILL GIVE THAT PERSON LIFE. BUT THERE IS A SIN THAT LEADS TO DEATH, AND I AM NOT SAYING YOU SHOULD PRAY FOR THOSE WHO COMMIT IT."
- 1 JOHN 5:16 -

My Personal Prayers...

FOR MY LOVED ONES

_____
_____
_____
_____
_____
_____
_____

FOR MY COLLEAGUES

_____
_____
_____
_____
_____
_____

WEEK 21: _____

FOR MY CITY

_____

_____

_____

_____

FOR MY STATE

_____

_____

_____

_____

FOR MY NATION

_____

_____

_____

_____

FOR THE WORLD

_____

_____

_____

_____

"THE NEXT DAY JOHN SAW JESUS COMING TOWARD HIM AND SAID, "LOOK! THE LAMB OF GOD WHO TAKES AWAY THE SIN OF THE WORLD!"
- JOHN 1:29 -

Abba Father,

DRAW ME CLOSER TO

_____
_____
_____
_____
_____

LEAD ME AWAY FROM

_____
_____
_____
_____

INCREASE MY DISCERNMENT IN

_____
_____
_____
_____
_____
_____

WEEK 22: _____

GIVE ME WISDOM TO

_____
_____
_____
_____
_____
_____
_____
_____
_____
_____
_____

GIVE ME STRENGTH TO

_____
_____
_____
_____
_____
_____
_____
_____
_____
_____
_____

"PUT ON YOUR NEW NATURE, AND BE RENEWED
AS YOU LEARN TO KNOW YOUR CREATOR AND
BECOME LIKE HIM."
- COLOSSIANS 3:10 -

Areas for Growth

5 THINGS I STRUGGLE WITH

1. _____
2. _____
3. _____
4. _____
5. _____

5 LIES I BELIEVE ABOUT ME

1. _____
2. _____
3. _____
4. _____
5. _____

5 TRUTHS GOD'S WORD REVEALS ABOUT ME

1. _____
2. _____
3. _____
4. _____
5. _____

WEEK 23: _____

5 SCRIPTURES TO MEDITATE ON

1. _____
2. _____
3. _____
4. _____
5. _____

5 DECLATIONS TO SPEAK OVER MY LIFE

1. _____
2. _____
3. _____
4. _____
5. _____

5 THINGS I AM BELIEVING GOD FOR

1. _____
2. _____
3. _____
4. _____
5. _____

5 WAYS I CAN SHARE MY FAITH IN JESUS WITH OTHERS

1. _____
2. _____
3. _____
4. _____
5. _____

"I PONDERED THE DIRECTION OF MY LIFE, AND I TURNED
TO FOLLOW YOUR LAWS."
- PSALMS 119:59 -

Moment of Reflection

I REMAINED FOCUSED BY

_____
_____
_____
_____
_____

I AVOIDED DISTRACTIONS BY

_____
_____
_____
_____
_____

I FELT GOD'S LOVE WHEN

_____
_____
_____
_____

WEEK 24: _____

I PRAISED GOD FOR

_____

_____

_____

_____

_____

I ASKED FORGIVENESS FOR

_____

_____

_____

_____

_____

I AM LOOKING FORWARD TO

_____

_____

_____

_____

_____

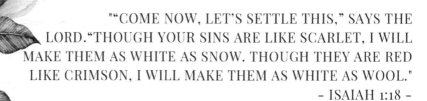

"'COME NOW, LET'S SETTLE THIS," SAYS THE
LORD. "THOUGH YOUR SINS ARE LIKE SCARLET, I WILL
MAKE THEM AS WHITE AS SNOW. THOUGH THEY ARE RED
LIKE CRIMSON, I WILL MAKE THEM AS WHITE AS WOOL."
- ISAIAH 1:18 -

My Reflection

_____
_____
_____
_____
_____
_____
_____
_____
_____
_____
_____
_____
_____
_____
_____
_____
_____
_____
_____
_____
_____

WEEK 25: _____

WHAT IS THIS PASSAGE TEACHING?

_____

_____

_____

_____

_____

HOW CAN I APPLY WHAT I HAVE LEARNED TO MY LIFE?

_____

_____

_____

_____

_____

WHAT IS HOLDING ME BACK FROM TAKING ACTION?

_____

_____

_____

_____

_____

MY PERSONAL PRAYER TO GOD

_____

_____

_____

_____

_____

Celebrate My Wins

WINS I AM THANKFUL FOR

1. _____
2. _____
3. _____
4. _____
5. _____

PEOPLE WHO HAVE HELPED ALONG THE WAY

1. _____
2. _____
3. _____
4. _____
5. _____

GREATEST LESSON LEARNED

_____
_____
_____
_____
_____
_____

WEEK 26: _____

WHY DO I *celebrate* THESE WINS?

_____
_____
_____
_____
_____
_____
_____
_____
_____
_____

HOW CAN I *help* OTHERS WIN?

_____
_____
_____
_____
_____
_____
_____
_____
_____
_____
_____

"PRAY IN THE SPIRIT AT ALL TIMES AND ON EVERY
OCCASION. STAY ALERT AND BE PERSISTENT IN YOUR
PRAYERS FOR ALL BELIEVERS EVERYWHERE."
- EPHESIANS 6:18 -

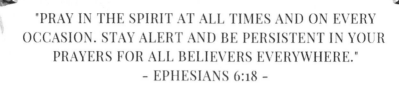

My Personal Prayers...

FOR MY LOVED ONES

_____
_____
_____
_____
_____
_____
_____
_____

FOR MY COLLEAGUES

_____
_____
_____
_____
_____
_____
_____

WEEK 27: _____

FOR MY CITY

_____
_____
_____
_____
_____

FOR MY STATE

_____
_____
_____
_____
_____

FOR MY NATION

_____
_____
_____
_____
_____

FOR THE WORLD

_____
_____
_____
_____
_____

"MAY THE GRACE OF THE LORD JESUS CHRIST, THE LOVE OF GOD, AND THE FELLOWSHIP OF THE HOLY SPIRIT BE WITH YOU ALL."
- 2 CORINTHIANS 13:14 -

Abba Father,

DRAW ME CLOSER TO

_____
_____
_____
_____
_____

LEAD ME AWAY FROM

_____
_____
_____
_____

INCREASE MY DISCERNMENT IN

_____
_____
_____
_____
_____

WEEK 28: _____

GIVE ME WISDOM TO

_____

_____

_____

_____

_____

_____

_____

_____

_____

_____

GIVE ME STRENGTH TO

_____

_____

_____

_____

_____

_____

_____

_____

_____

_____

"THIS MEANS THAT ANYONE WHO BELONGS TO
CHRIST HAS BECOME A NEW PERSON. THE OLD LIFE
IS GONE; A NEW LIFE HAS BEGUN!"
- 2 CORINTHIANS 5:17 -

Areas for Growth

5 THINGS I STRUGGLE WITH

1. _____
2. _____
3. _____
4. _____
5. _____

5 LIES I BELIEVE ABOUT ME

1. _____
2. _____
3. _____
4. _____
5. _____

5 TRUTHS GOD'S WORD REVEALS ABOUT ME

1. _____
2. _____
3. _____
4. _____
5. _____

WEEK 29: _____

5 SCRIPTURES TO MEDITATE ON

1. _____
2. _____
3. _____
4. _____
5. _____

5 DECLATIONS TO SPEAK OVER MY LIFE

1. _____
2. _____
3. _____
4. _____
5. _____

5 THINGS I AM BELIEVING GOD FOR

1. _____
2. _____
3. _____
4. _____
5. _____

5 WAYS I CAN SHARE MY FAITH IN JESUS WITH OTHERS

1. _____
2. _____
3. _____
4. _____
5. _____

"THAT IS WHY YOU SHOULD EXAMINE YOURSELF BEFORE
EATING THE BREAD AND DRINKING THE CUP."
- 1 CORINTHIANS 11:28 -

Moment of Reflection

I REMAINED FOCUSED BY

_____
_____
_____
_____
_____

I AVOIDED DISTRACTIONS BY

_____
_____
_____
_____
_____

I FELT GOD'S LOVE WHEN

_____
_____
_____
_____

WEEK 30: _____

I PRAISED GOD FOR

_____

_____

_____

_____

_____

I ASKED FORGIVENESS FOR

_____

_____

_____

_____

_____

I AM LOOKING FORWARD TO

_____

_____

_____

_____

_____

"DON'T USE FOUL OR ABUSIVE LANGUAGE. LET
EVERYTHING YOU SAY BE GOOD AND HELPFUL, SO
THAT YOUR WORDS WILL BE AN ENCOURAGEMENT
TO THOSE WHO HEAR THEM."
- EPHESIANS 4:29 -

My Reflection

_____

_____

_____

_____

_____

_____

_____

_____

_____

_____

_____

_____

_____

_____

_____

_____

_____

_____

_____

WEEK 31: _____

WHAT IS THIS PASSAGE TEACHING?

_____

_____

_____

_____

_____

HOW CAN I APPLY WHAT I HAVE LEARNED TO MY LIFE?

_____

_____

_____

_____

_____

WHAT IS HOLDING ME BACK FROM TAKING ACTION?

_____

_____

_____

_____

_____

MY PERSONAL PRAYER TO GOD

_____

_____

_____

_____

_____

Celebrate My Wins

WINS I AM THANKFUL FOR

1. _____
2. _____
3. _____
4. _____
5. _____

PEOPLE WHO HAVE HELPED ALONG THE WAY

1. _____
2. _____
3. _____
4. _____
5. _____

GREATEST LESSON LEARNED

_____
_____
_____
_____
_____
_____

WEEK 32: _____

WHY DO I *celebrate* THESE WINS?

_____
_____
_____
_____
_____
_____
_____
_____
_____
_____

HOW CAN I *help* OTHERS WIN?

_____
_____
_____
_____
_____
_____
_____
_____
_____
_____
_____

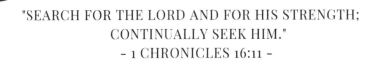

My Personal Prayers...

FOR MY LOVED ONES

_____
_____
_____
_____
_____
_____
_____
_____

FOR MY COLLEAGUES

_____
_____
_____
_____
_____
_____
_____

WEEK 33: _____

FOR MY CITY

_____

_____

_____

_____

_____

FOR MY STATE

_____

_____

_____

_____

FOR MY NATION

_____

_____

_____

_____

FOR THE WORLD

_____

_____

_____

_____

_____

"YOU ARE WORTHY, O LORD OUR GOD, TO RECEIVE GLORY AND
HONOR AND POWER. FOR YOU CREATED ALL THINGS, AND THEY
EXIST BECAUSE YOU CREATED WHAT YOU PLEASED."
- REVELATION 4:11 -

Abba Father,

DRAW ME CLOSER TO

_____

_____

_____

_____

_____

LEAD ME AWAY FROM

_____

_____

_____

_____

_____

INCREASE MY DISCERNMENT IN

_____

_____

_____

_____

_____

WEEK 34: _____

GIVE ME WISDOM TO

_____

_____

_____

_____

_____

_____

_____

_____

_____

_____

GIVE ME STRENGTH TO

_____

_____

_____

_____

_____

_____

_____

_____

_____

_____

Areas for Growth

5 THINGS I STRUGGLE WITH

1. _____
2. _____
3. _____
4. _____
5. _____

5 LIES I BELIEVE ABOUT ME

1. _____
2. _____
3. _____
4. _____
5. _____

5 TRUTHS GOD'S WORD REVEALS ABOUT ME

1. _____
2. _____
3. _____
4. _____
5. _____

WEEK 35: _____

5 SCRIPTURES TO MEDITATE ON

1. _____
2. _____
3. _____
4. _____
5. _____

5 DECLATIONS TO SPEAK OVER MY LIFE

1. _____
2. _____
3. _____
4. _____
5. _____

5 THINGS I AM BELIEVING GOD FOR

1. _____
2. _____
3. _____
4. _____
5. _____

5 WAYS I CAN SHARE MY FAITH IN JESUS WITH OTHERS

1. _____
2. _____
3. _____
4. _____
5. _____

"BUT IF WE CONFESS OUR SINS TO HIM, HE IS FAITHFUL
AND JUST TO FORGIVE US OUR SINS AND TO CLEANSE US
FROM ALL WICKEDNESS."
- 1 JOHN 1:9 -

Moment of Reflection

I REMAINED FOCUSED BY

_____
_____
_____
_____
_____
_____

I AVOIDED DISTRACTIONS BY

_____
_____
_____
_____
_____

I FELT GOD'S LOVE WHEN

_____
_____
_____
_____

WEEK 36: _____

I PRAISED GOD FOR

_____

_____

_____

_____

_____

I ASKED FORGIVENESS FOR

_____

_____

_____

_____

_____

I AM LOOKING FORWARD TO

_____

_____

_____

_____

_____

"GIVE, AND YOU WILL RECEIVE. YOUR GIFT WILL RETURN TO YOU IN FULL—PRESSED DOWN, SHAKEN TOGETHER TO MAKE ROOM FOR MORE, RUNNING OVER, AND POURED INTO YOUR LAP. THE AMOUNT YOU GIVE WILL DETERMINE THE AMOUNT YOU GET BACK"

- LUKE 6:38 -

My Reflection

WEEK 37: _____

WHAT IS THIS PASSAGE TEACHING?

_____

_____

_____

_____

_____

HOW CAN I APPLY WHAT I HAVE LEARNED TO MY LIFE?

_____

_____

_____

_____

_____

WHAT IS HOLDING ME BACK FROM TAKING ACTION?

_____

_____

_____

_____

_____

MY PERSONAL PRAYER TO GOD

_____

_____

_____

_____

_____

Celebrate My Wins

WINS I AM THANKFUL FOR

1. _____
2. _____
3. _____
4. _____
5. _____

PEOPLE WHO HAVE HELPED ALONG THE WAY

1. _____
2. _____
3. _____
4. _____
5. _____

GREATEST LESSON LEARNED

_____
_____
_____
_____
_____
_____

WEEK 38: _____

WHY DO I *celebrate* THESE WINS?

_____
_____
_____
_____
_____
_____
_____
_____
_____
_____
_____

HOW CAN I *help* OTHERS WIN?

_____
_____
_____
_____
_____
_____
_____
_____
_____
_____
_____

"DON'T WORRY ABOUT ANYTHING; INSTEAD, PRAY ABOUT
EVERYTHING. TELL GOD WHAT YOU NEED, AND THANK
HIM FOR ALL HE HAS DONE."
- PHILIPPIANS 4:6 -

My Personal Prayers...

FOR MY LOVED ONES

_____
_____
_____
_____
_____
_____
_____
_____

FOR MY COLLEAGUES

_____
_____
_____
_____
_____
_____

WEEK 39: _____

FOR MY CITY

_____

_____

_____

_____

_____

FOR MY STATE

_____

_____

_____

_____

_____

FOR MY NATION

_____

_____

_____

_____

_____

FOR THE WORLD

_____

_____

_____

_____

_____

Abba Father,

DRAW ME CLOSER TO

_____
_____
_____
_____
_____

LEAD ME AWAY FROM

_____
_____
_____
_____

INCREASE MY DISCERNMENT IN

_____
_____
_____
_____
_____

WEEK 40: _____

GIVE ME WISDOM TO

_____

_____

_____

_____

_____

_____

_____

_____

_____

GIVE ME STRENGTH TO

_____

_____

_____

_____

_____

_____

_____

_____

_____

_____

"BUT DON'T JUST LISTEN TO GOD'S WORD. YOU MUST
DO WHAT IT SAYS. OTHERWISE, YOU ARE ONLY
FOOLING YOURSELVES."
- JAMES 1:22 -

Areas for Growth

5 THINGS I STRUGGLE WITH

1. _____
2. _____
3. _____
4. _____
5. _____

5 LIES I BELIEVE ABOUT ME

1. _____
2. _____
3. _____
4. _____
5. _____

5 TRUTHS GOD'S WORD REVEALS ABOUT ME

1. _____
2. _____
3. _____
4. _____
5. _____

WEEK 41: _____

5 SCRIPTURES TO MEDITATE ON

1. _____
2. _____
3. _____
4. _____
5. _____

5 DECLATIONS TO SPEAK OVER MY LIFE

1. _____
2. _____
3. _____
4. _____
5. _____

5 THINGS I AM BELIEVING GOD FOR

1. _____
2. _____
3. _____
4. _____
5. _____

5 WAYS I CAN SHARE MY FAITH IN JESUS WITH OTHERS

1. _____
2. _____
3. _____
4. _____
5. _____

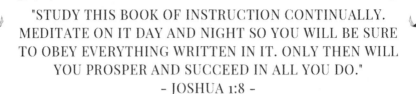

"STUDY THIS BOOK OF INSTRUCTION CONTINUALLY.
MEDITATE ON IT DAY AND NIGHT SO YOU WILL BE SURE
TO OBEY EVERYTHING WRITTEN IN IT. ONLY THEN WILL
YOU PROSPER AND SUCCEED IN ALL YOU DO."
- JOSHUA 1:8 -

Moment of Reflection

I REMAINED FOCUSED BY

_____

_____

_____

_____

_____

I AVOIDED DISTRACTIONS BY

_____

_____

_____

_____

_____

I FELT GOD'S LOVE WHEN

_____

_____

_____

_____

WEEK 42: _____

I PRAISED GOD FOR

_____

_____

_____

_____

_____

I ASKED FORGIVENESS FOR

_____

_____

_____

_____

_____

I AM LOOKING FORWARD TO

_____

_____

_____

_____

_____

"NO ONE CAN SERVE TWO MASTERS. FOR YOU WILL
HATE ONE AND LOVE THE OTHER; YOU WILL BE
DEVOTED TO ONE AND DESPISE THE OTHER. YOU
CANNOT SERVE GOD AND BE ENSLAVED TO MONEY."
– MATTHEW 6:24 –

My Reflection

WEEK 43: _____

WHAT IS THIS PASSAGE TEACHING?

_____

_____

_____

_____

_____

HOW CAN I APPLY WHAT I HAVE LEARNED TO MY LIFE?

_____

_____

_____

_____

_____

WHAT IS HOLDING ME BACK FROM TAKING ACTION?

_____

_____

_____

_____

_____

MY PERSONAL PRAYER TO GOD

_____

_____

_____

_____

_____

Celebrate My Wins

WINS I AM THANKFUL FOR

1. _____
2. _____
3. _____
4. _____
5. _____

PEOPLE WHO HAVE HELPED ALONG THE WAY

1. _____
2. _____
3. _____
4. _____
5. _____

GREATEST LESSON LEARNED

_____
_____
_____
_____
_____
_____

WEEK 44: _____

WHY DO I *celebrate* THESE WINS?

_____
_____
_____
_____
_____
_____
_____
_____
_____
_____

HOW CAN I *help* OTHERS WIN?

_____
_____
_____
_____
_____
_____
_____
_____
_____
_____

"DEVOTE YOURSELVES TO PRAYER WITH AN ALERT
MIND AND A THANKFUL HEART."
- COLOSSIANS 4:2 -

My Personal Prayers...

FOR MY LOVED ONES

_____
_____
_____
_____
_____
_____
_____
_____

FOR MY COLLEAGUES

_____
_____
_____
_____
_____
_____
_____

WEEK 45: _____

FOR MY CITY

FOR MY STATE

FOR MY NATION

FOR THE WORLD

Abba Father,

DRAW ME CLOSER TO

_____

_____

_____

_____

_____

LEAD ME AWAY FROM

_____

_____

_____

_____

INCREASE MY DISCERNMENT IN

_____

_____

_____

_____

_____

_____

WEEK 46: _____

GIVE ME WISDOM TO

_____

_____

_____

_____

_____

_____

_____

_____

_____

_____

GIVE ME STRENGTH TO

_____

_____

_____

_____

_____

_____

_____

_____

_____

_____

"AFTER THIS PRAYER, THE MEETING PLACE SHOOK, AND THEY WERE ALL FILLED WITH THE HOLY SPIRIT. THEN THEY PREACHED THE WORD OF GOD WITH BOLDNESS."
- ACTS 4:31-

Areas for Growth

5 THINGS I STRUGGLE WITH

1. _____
2. _____
3. _____
4. _____
5. _____

5 LIES I BELIEVE ABOUT ME

1. _____
2. _____
3. _____
4. _____
5. _____

5 TRUTHS GOD'S WORD REVEALS ABOUT ME

1. _____
2. _____
3. _____
4. _____
5. _____

WEEK 47: _____

5 SCRIPTURES TO MEDITATE ON

1. _____
2. _____
3. _____
4. _____
5. _____

5 DECLATIONS TO SPEAK OVER MY LIFE

1. _____
2. _____
3. _____
4. _____
5. _____

5 THINGS I AM BELIEVING GOD FOR

1. _____
2. _____
3. _____
4. _____
5. _____

5 WAYS I CAN SHARE MY FAITH IN JESUS WITH OTHERS

1. _____
2. _____
3. _____
4. _____
5. _____

"AND YOU WILL KNOW THE TRUTH, AND THE TRUTH WILL
SET YOU FREE."
- JOHN 8:32 -

Moment of Reflection

I REMAINED FOCUSED BY

_____
_____
_____
_____
_____

I AVOIDED DISTRACTIONS BY

_____
_____
_____
_____
_____

I FELT GOD'S LOVE WHEN

_____
_____
_____
_____

WEEK 48: _____

I PRAISED GOD FOR

_____

_____

_____

_____

_____

I ASKED FORGIVENESS FOR

_____

_____

_____

_____

_____

I AM LOOKING FORWARD TO

_____

_____

_____

_____

_____

"DON'T LET ANYONE THINK LESS OF YOU BECAUSE YOU ARE YOUNG. BE AN EXAMPLE TO ALL BELIEVERS IN WHAT YOU SAY, IN THE WAY YOU LIVE, IN YOUR LOVE, YOUR FAITH, AND YOUR PURITY."
- 1 TIMOTHY 4:12 -

My Reflection

_____

_____

_____

_____

_____

_____

_____

_____

_____

_____

_____

_____

_____

_____

_____

_____

_____

_____

_____

WEEK 49: _____

WHAT IS THIS PASSAGE TEACHING?

_____

_____

_____

_____

_____

HOW CAN I APPLY WHAT I HAVE LEARNED TO MY LIFE?

_____

_____

_____

_____

_____

WHAT IS HOLDING ME BACK FROM TAKING ACTION?

_____

_____

_____

_____

_____

MY PERSONAL PRAYER TO GOD

_____

_____

_____

_____

_____

"SO NOW THERE IS NO CONDEMNATION FOR THOSE WHO BELONG TO CHRIST JESUS. AND BECAUSE YOU BELONG TO HIM, THE POWER OF THE LIFE-GIVING SPIRIT HAS FREED YOU FROM THE POWER OF SIN THAT LEADS TO DEATH."
- ROMANS 8:1-2 -

Celebrate My Wins

WINS I AM THANKFUL FOR

1. _____
2. _____
3. _____
4. _____
5. _____

PEOPLE WHO HAVE HELPED ALONG THE WAY

1. _____
2. _____
3. _____
4. _____
5. _____

GREATEST LESSON LEARNED

_____
_____
_____
_____
_____

WEEK 50: _____

WHY DO I *celebrate* THESE WINS?

_____
_____
_____
_____
_____
_____
_____
_____
_____
_____

HOW CAN I *help* OTHERS WIN?

_____
_____
_____
_____
_____
_____
_____
_____
_____
_____

"BUT WHEN YOU PRAY, GO AWAY BY YOURSELF, SHUT
THE DOOR BEHIND YOU, AND PRAY TO YOUR FATHER IN
PRIVATE. THEN YOUR FATHER, WHO SEES EVERYTHING,
WILL REWARD YOU."
- MATTHEW 6:6 -

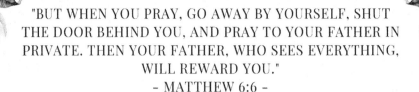

FOR MY LOVED ONES

_____
_____
_____
_____
_____
_____
_____
_____
_____
_____

FOR MY COLLEAGUES

_____
_____
_____
_____
_____
_____
_____
_____

WEEK 51: _____

FOR MY CITY

_____
_____
_____
_____
_____

FOR MY STATE

_____
_____
_____
_____
_____

FOR MY NATION

_____
_____
_____
_____
_____

FOR THE WORLD

_____
_____
_____
_____
_____

"ABRAHAM NAMED THE PLACE YAHWEH-YIREH (WHICH MEANS "THE LORD WILL PROVIDE"). TO THIS DAY, PEOPLE STILL USE THAT NAME AS A PROVERB: "ON THE MOUNTAIN OF THE LORD IT WILL BE PROVIDED."
- GENESIS 22:14 -

Abba Father,

DRAW ME CLOSER TO

_____

_____

_____

_____

_____

LEAD ME AWAY FROM

_____

_____

_____

_____

INCREASE MY DISCERNMENT IN

_____

_____

_____

_____

_____

WEEK 52: _____

GIVE ME WISDOM TO

_____

_____

_____

_____

_____

_____

_____

_____

_____

_____

_____

_____

GIVE ME STRENGTH TO

_____

_____

_____

_____

_____

_____

_____

_____

_____

_____

_____

_____

"WHEN I WAS A CHILD, I SPOKE AND THOUGHT AND REASONED AS A CHILD. BUT WHEN I GREW UP, I PUT AWAY CHILDISH THINGS."
- 1 CORINTHIANS 13:11 -

Areas for Growth

5 THINGS I STRUGGLE WITH

1. _____
2. _____
3. _____
4. _____
5. _____

5 LIES I BELIEVE ABOUT ME

1. _____
2. _____
3. _____
4. _____
5. _____

5 TRUTHS GOD'S WORD REVEALS ABOUT ME

1. _____
2. _____
3. _____
4. _____
5. _____

WEEK 53: _____

5 SCRIPTURES TO MEDITATE ON

1. _____
2. _____
3. _____
4. _____
5. _____

5 DECLATIONS TO SPEAK OVER MY LIFE

1. _____
2. _____
3. _____
4. _____
5. _____

5 THINGS I AM BELIEVING GOD FOR

1. _____
2. _____
3. _____
4. _____
5. _____

5 WAYS I CAN SHARE MY FAITH IN JESUS WITH OTHERS

1. _____
2. _____
3. _____
4. _____
5. _____

"FOR GOD IS WORKING IN YOU, GIVING YOU THE DESIRE
AND THE POWER TO DO WHAT PLEASES HIM."
- PHILIPPIANS 2:13 -

Moment of Reflection

I REMAINED FOCUSED BY

_____
_____
_____
_____
_____

I AVOIDED DISTRACTIONS BY

_____
_____
_____
_____
_____

I FELT GOD'S LOVE WHEN

_____
_____
_____
_____

WEEK 54: _____

I PRAISED GOD FOR

_____

_____

_____

_____

_____

I ASKED FORGIVENESS FOR

_____

_____

_____

_____

_____

I AM LOOKING FORWARD TO

_____

_____

_____

_____

_____

Notes

_____
_____
_____
_____
_____
_____
_____
_____
_____
_____
_____
_____
_____
_____
_____
_____
_____
_____
_____
_____
_____
_____
_____

About the Author

Erica N. Williams is the founder of Journey to Purity®. She is the author of two books, including *Don't Give Up: A 7-Day Devotional Journey for Women* (released September 2019).

Having remained abstinent for more than 9 years, surviving molestation and losing her dad as a young girl, Erica stands strong in her faith.

A Purity Advocate and Coach whose goal is to help women remain focused and committed to their purity journey, Erica has been featured in The *Washington Post* and *The Lily*. She is passionate about Jesus' healing, restorative, and redemptive power and loves sharing this message through writing, speaking and mentoring women.

To connect with Erica daily or book a one-on-one consultation, visit:

Website: www.ericanwilliams.com
Facebook: fb.me/officialericanwilliams
Instagram: @ericanwilliams

About Journey to Purity®

Erica N. Williams is the founder of Journey to Purity®, based in Woodbridge, Virginia.

If you were encouraged by *With God's Help I Will* and desire to grow spiritually, mentally, physically, emotionally and financially, we can help.

Journey to Purity® is your all-access membership designed to help you live, learn and thrive on your purity journey all while gaining support and encouragement from a community of like-minded women.

Ready to take your Christian journey to new heights? Visit www.journeytopuritymovement.com to learn more.

To receive daily encouragement for your journey, follow Journey to Purity® on social media:

Facebook: fb.me/journeytopurity
Instagram: @journeytopurity

Made in the USA
Las Vegas, NV
15 April 2022